W9-CAN-357

TOUGH TRUCKS

Written by Sonia Sander
& Illustrated by Rick Courtney

SCHOLASTIC INC.
New York Toronto London Auckland Sydney
Mexico City New Delhi Hong Kong Buenos Aires

No part of this publication may be reproduced, stored in a retrieval system,
or transmitted in any form or by any means, electronic, mechanical,
photocopying, recording, or otherwise, without written permission of the publisher.
For information regarding permission, write to Scholastic Inc.,
Attention: Permissions Department, 557 Broadway, New York, NY 10012.

TONKA™: Tractor Tracks, ISBN 0-439-91820-0, Copyright © 2007 by Hasbro.
TONKA™: Get Set to Wreck!, ISBN 0-439-91822-7, Copyright © 2007 by Hasbro.
TONKA™: Mix It Up!, ISBN 0-439-91824-3, Copyright © 2007 by Hasbro.
TONKA™: Stop! Road Block!, ISBN 0-439-91825-1, Copyright © 2007 by Hasbro.
TONKA™: Dump Truck Dump!, ISBN 0-439-91826-X, Copyright © 2007 by Hasbro.
TONKA™: Raise the Crane!, ISBN 0-439-91827-8, Copyright © 2007 by Hasbro.
TONKA™: Beep! Beep!, ISBN 0-439-91828-6, Copyright © 2007 by Hasbro.
TONKA™: Fire Siren, ISBN 0-439-91829-4, Copyright © 2007 by Hasbro.
TONKA™: Slow Tow Home, ISBN 0-439-91830-8, Copyright © 2007 by Hasbro.
TONKA™: Go, Trucks, Go!, ISBN 0-439-91831-6, Copyright © 2007 by Hasbro.
TONKA™: Trash Dash, ISBN 0-439-91832-4, Copyright © 2007 by Hasbro.
TONKA™: Truck It In!, ISBN 0-439-91833-2, Copyright © 2007 by Hasbro.

HASBRO and its logo and TONKA are trademarks of Hasbro
and are used with permission.© 2008 Hasbro. All rights reserved.

Under license by Scholastic Inc. Published by Scholastic Inc.
SCHOLASTIC and associated logos are trademarks and/or registered trademarks of Scholastic Inc.

ISBN-13: 978-0-545-12052-4
ISBN: 0-545-12052-7

12 11 10 9 8 7 6 5 4 3 2   9 10 11/0

Printed in Singapore   46
This compilation edition first printing, December 2008

Welcome to the Tonka®
Phonics Reading Program!

Learning to read is so important for your child's success in school and in life. Now **Tonka**® is here to help your child learn important phonics skills. Here's how these readers work:

Take phonics, the fundamental skill of knowing that the letters we read represent the sounds we hear and say. Add **Tonka**® and help your child LEARN to read and LOVE to read!

To be a good reader, it takes practice. That's where **Tonka**® can make a difference. Kids love **Tonka**® vehicles and will want to read about them over and over again. Try these ideas for enjoying the books with your child:

 Read together by taking turns line by line or page by page.

 Look for all the words that have the sound being featured in the reader. Read them over and over again.

 Let your child read the story to you and then retell it in his or her own words.

Scholastic has been helping families encourage young readers for more than 80 years. Thank you for letting us help you support your beginning reader.

Happy reading,
Francie Alexander,
Chief Academic Officer, Scholastic Inc.

TABLE OF
CONTENTS

▰▰▰▰▰▰▰▰▰▰▰▰▰▰▰

▰▰▰▰▰▰▰▰▰▰▰▰

In this story, you can learn all about the <u>short a</u> sound. Here are some words to sound out.

land   **after**   **can**

plant   **tractor**   **drag**

These are words that you will see in this story and many other stories. You will want to learn them as well.

across   grow   the   again   now

Book 1 - short a

Tractor Tracks

I am a **tractor**.
I **drag** my plow
across the **land**.

I **can plant** the seeds.

I **plant** the seeds **after** the **land** is **watered**.

I **can** feed the **plants**.

Then I **stand back** as the **plants** grow.

Now it is time to **snap** the **plants** up.

I **can drag** my bucket to **catch** the corn.

Next year I **can** go
back and **plant** again.

In this story, you can learn all about the <u>short e</u> sound. Here are some words to sound out.

wreck	**get**	**send**
let's	**metal**	**mess**

These are words that you will see in this story and many other stories. You will want to learn them as well.

ball into my all what

Book 2 - short e

Get Set to Wreck!

I am a crane.
I have a **wrecking** ball.
I do my **best** to make
a **mess**!

Let's get set to wreck!

Let's send the **metal** ball flying.

Let's wreck the windows.

Then let's send the bricks into the air.

Next let's flatten all the steps.

Let's get rid of the **rest**.

What can we **wreck next**?

In this story, you can learn all about the <u>short i</u> sound. Here are some words to sound out.

spin	**big**	**hill**
dig	**sit**	**mix**

These are words that you will see in this story and many other stories. You will want to learn them as well.

slide   next   around   wait   over

Book 3 - short i

Mix It Up!

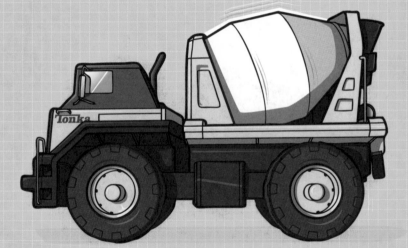

I am a **big
mixer** truck.
I have a **big list**
of **things** to do.

First I **fill** up
my drum.
In goes the **mix**.

I **spin** my drum
around and around.
Mix! Mix! Mix!

I **zip** up a **big hill**.
My drum **still spins**.
Spin! Spin! Spin!

I **sit** and wait
for a truck to
dig a **big pit**.

Then I **tip** my
slide over the **pit**.

I let the **mix spill** out **into** the **pit.** **Drip! Drip! Drip!**

It is time to **fill** up for my next job.

In this story, you can learn all about the <u>short o</u> sound. Here are some words to sound out.

stop   **plop**   **job**

rocks   **pond**   **drop**

These are words that you will see in this story and many other stories. You will want to learn them as well.

truck   have   car   road   open

Book 4 - short o

Stop! Road Block!

I am a police car.
I have **got** a **job** to do.

A **lot** of **rocks dropped** on the road.

The **rocks blocked** the road. **Honk! Honk!**

The road is **not** open.
Stop!

A truck **stops** near the **spot** where the **rocks dropped**.

The truck **knocks** the **rocks** off the road.

The **rocks drop**
in a **pond.**
Plop! Plop! Plop!

Great **job**!

In this story, you can learn all about the <u>short u</u> sound. Here are some words to sound out.

truck   **dump**   **stuff**
hum   **lug**   **fun**

These are words that you will see in this story and many other stories. You will want to learn them as well.

and   **they**   **my**   **up**   **with**

Dump Truck Dump!

I am a **dump truck**.
I **lug** and **dump stuff**.

I hum as I run.
Hum! Hum! Hum!

Trucks fill me **up** with **stuff** they **dug up**.

I chug up the bumps.
Chug! Chug! Chug!

Up top, I **dump** out my **stuff**.

Then I **must**
tug up my bed.

I **must lug** and
dump more **stuff**.

It's so **much fun** to **dump stuff!**

In this story, you can learn all about the <u>long a</u> sound. Here are some words to sound out.

crane   **shake**   **place**

raise   **make**   **chain**

These are words that you will see in this story and many other stories. You will want to learn them as well.

hook   air   into   down   arm

Tonka
PHONICS READING PROGRAM

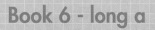

Raise the Crane!

I am a **crane**.
I **take great** big loads
up into the air.

I help **make**
skyscrapers.

I **wait** as **they** hook up my load.

I **raise** up my arm.
My **chain shakes** down.
Shake, shake, shake.

I take aim.
I place the bar
in its space.

I **wait** for the
pane of glass.

Later, I raise my arm to put in the **pane**.

It **takes** a lot of work
to **make** a **skyscraper!**

In this story, you can learn all about the <u>long e</u> sound. Here are some words to sound out.

beep　　**speed**　　**need**

wheel　　**team**　　**even**

These are words that you will see in this story and many other stories. You will want to learn them as well.

rides　**call**　**them**　**rescue**　**back**

Beep! Beep!

I am an ambulance.
See me speed
down the **street**!
Vroom!

Hear my siren **scream**.
Beep! Beep!

A rescue **team**
rides inside of **me**.

I **need** to be kept **neat** and **clean**.

People who **need** help call **me**.
I **speed** to **reach** them.

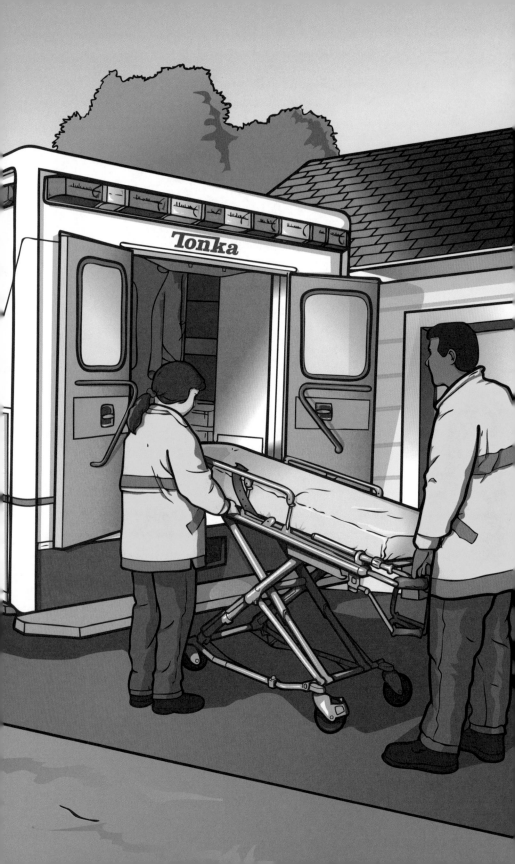

The rescue **team** can **even wheel** out a bed.

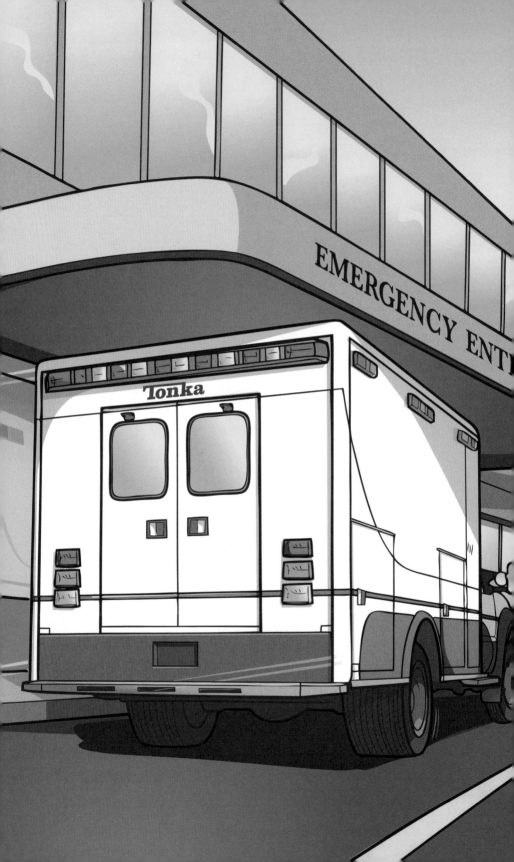

Then I **speed** back
to the hospital.

I **need** to **speed** away again!
Beep! Beep!

In this story, you can learn all about the <u>long i</u> sound. Here are some words to sound out.

fire	**slide**	**time**
tight	**drive**	**size**

These are words that you will see in this story and many other stories. You will want to learn them as well.

alarm fast loud hold home

Fire Siren

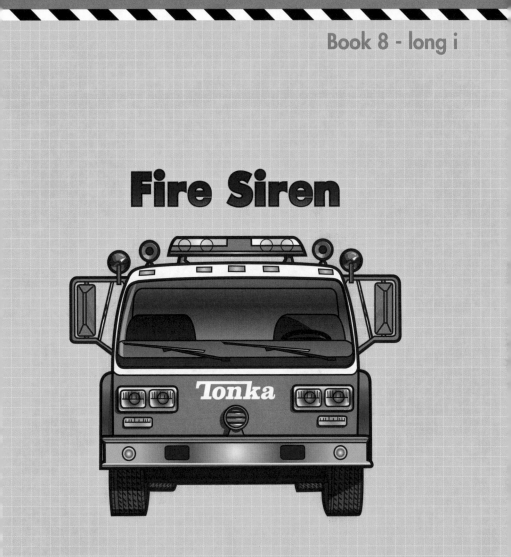

I am a **fire** truck!
I shine red.

The **fire** alarm rings.
Firefighters slide
down the pole.

Firefighters climb
up my **sides**.
They hold on **tight**.

My **siren** is loud.
My **lights** shine.

I **drive** fast to **arrive** at the **fire** in **time**.

It is a big-**size fire**.
I use all my hoses.

The **fire** is out.
I drive back home.

The **fire** alarm rings
again.
I ride into the **night**.

In this story, you can learn all about the <u>long o</u> sound. Here are some words to sound out.

low	**drove**	**tow**
hope	**slowly**	**home**

These are words that you will see in this story and many other stories. You will want to learn them as well.

to it car up with

Slow Tow Home

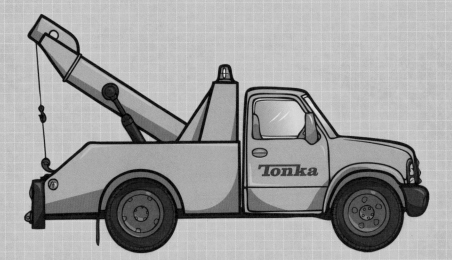

A car is **broken**
on the **road**.

I drove to tow
it home.

I **slowly** parked
close to the car.

I put my **towrope low** on the car.

I **slowly towed**
the car up.

I drove home slowly with the car.

Back at **home**,
I **unloaded** the car.

I **hope** the **broken** car
can be fixed. Soon I will
drive out to **tow** again.

In this story, you can learn all about <u>plurals</u>.
Here are some words to sound out.

trucks   **tires**   **lots**

holes   **streets**   **rocks**

These are words that you will see in this story and many other stories. You will want to learn them as well.

one   **can**   **will**   **move**   **main**

Go, Trucks, Go!

One truck drives
up the main street.
Go, truck, go!

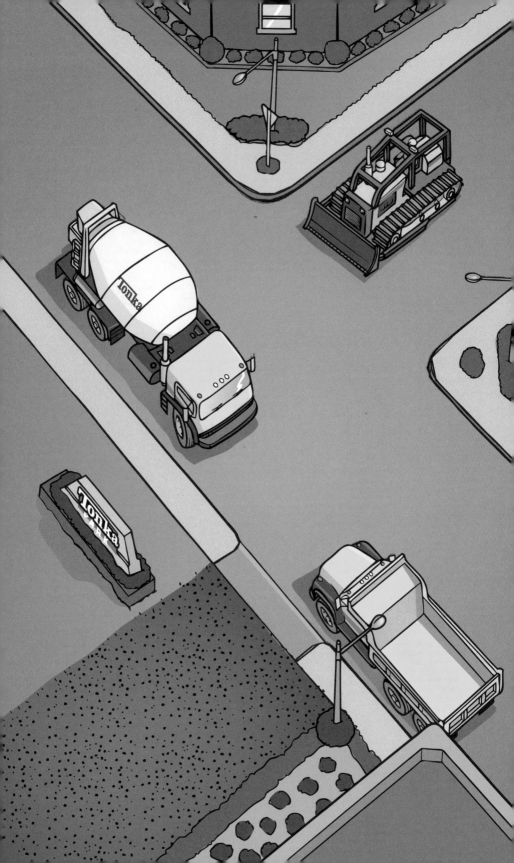

Two **trucks** drive
up the side **streets**.
Go, **trucks**, go!

I am a bulldozer.
I can move a
rock or tree.
Go, bulldozer, go!

I am a dump truck.
I can move **lots** of
rocks and **trees**.
Go, dump truck, go!

I am a front loader.
I am digging a hole.
I will dig three more
holes.

I am a cement mixer.
I can fill all four **holes**.
Go, mixer truck, go!

I am a dump truck.
I can move **lots** of
old **tires**.

The playground is finished
with **towers** of **tires**!
Go, **trucks**, go!

In this story, you can learn all about the <u>sh</u> sound. Here are some words to sound out.

trash	**sharp**	**flash**
shake	**shut**	**wash**

These are words that you will see in this story and many other stories. You will want to learn them as well.

street   **garbage**   **time**   **jaws**   **pick**

Trash Dash

I am a garbage truck.
It is time for me
to pick up the **trash**.

I **dash** up the
street in a **flash**.

They **shake** the **trash**
out of the cans into me.
Shake! Shake! Shake!

The **trash** cans
crash to the street.
Crash!

My **sharp** jaws **smash** **shut** on the **trash**. **Smash! Smash!**

I crush up the trash.
Crush! Crush!

I **rush** the **trash**
to the dump.

Now I need a **wash**.
Splash!

In this story, you can learn all about the <u>ck</u> sound. Here are some words to sound out.

truck   **rock**   **back**
pick   **stuck**   **bricks**

These are words that you will see in this story and many other stories. You will want to learn them as well.

into front can out some

Truck It In!

A **rock** is **stuck**
in the **muck**.
We need a **truck**!

I am a bulldozer.
I can **knock** the **rock**
out of the **muck**.

I am a front loader **truck**.
I can **pick** up the **rock**.

I can drop the **rock** into the **back** of the dump **truck**.

I am a mixer **truck**.
I can **stick** cement
in the hole.

I am a dump **truck**.
I can **back** in, too.
I can dump out **bricks**.

The workers can **stack** the **bricks**. They **stick bricks** with some cement.

Check out the house of **bricks**!

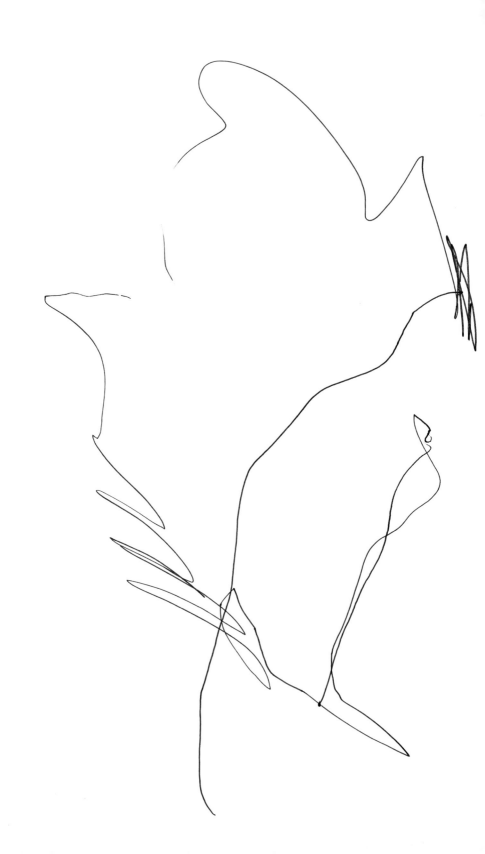

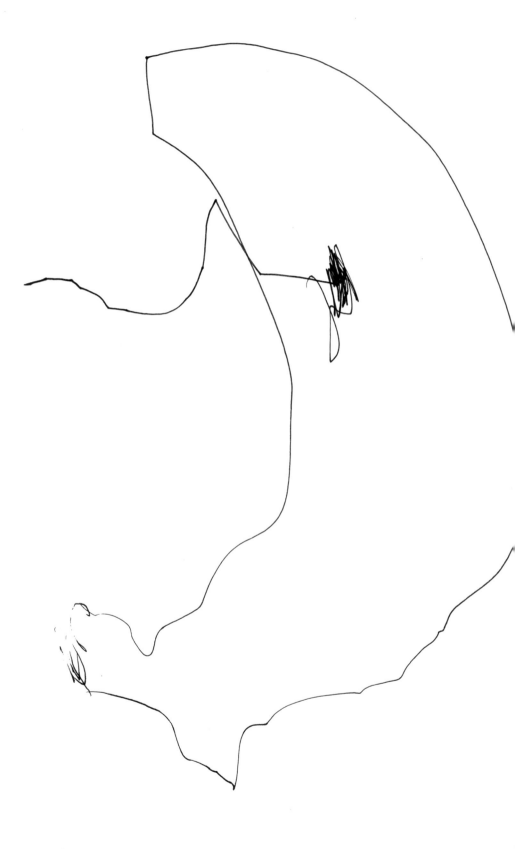